PRAISE FOR

THE LEGEND OF THE CHINESE ZODIAC

'An exquisitely illustrated picture book explaining the charming
Buddhist legend behind the twelve Chinese year names and even giving
the reason why there is no Year of the Cat. *The Legend of the Chinese Zodiac*
is also a gentle way to start talking with young children about the rich
variety of people's personalities' — ***The Times***

'If you want to find out how Buddha created the whole of the Chinese
zodiac – plus check out which animal governs your own year of birth, and
what particular qualities that gives you, make a bee-line for this colourful
and informative retelling of the ancient legend' — ***Books Magazine***

'Glowing, fluid pictures, a charming story and notes on the animals'
qualities add up to a book with masses of mileage' — ***Time Out***

'The Chinese animal zodiac and its roots are explained in clear, sharp
language, and details of the qualities of people born under the various
signs are great to compare with your friends…Fascinating stuff even
for adult readers' — ***Bookshelf***

05531

05531.

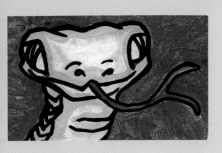

THE LEGEND
- OF THE -
CHINESE ZODIAC

written by
SUSAN WHITFIELD

illustrated by
PHILIPPA-ALYS BROWNE

BAREFOOT BOOKS

BATH

Barefoot Books Ltd
PO Box 95
Kingswood
Bristol BS30 5BH
This book has been printed on 100% acid-free paper
Text copyright © 1997 by Susan Whitfield
Illustrations copyright © 1997 by Philippa-Alys Browne
First published in Great Britain in 1997 by Barefoot Books Ltd. Reprinted in 1999.

ISBN 1 901223 51 5 Hardback
ISBN 1 901223 32 9 Paperback

Graphic design by Design/Section, Frome
Colour reproduction by Grafiscan, Italy
Printed and bound in Singapore

One summer's day, many hundreds of years ago, Buddha decided to give every year a name so that it would be easy to tell one year from another. But although he thought very hard he could not decide what to call them. He still had not made up his mind when he began to feel rather unwell and had to go to bed.

月 3 日

Although Buddha's closest friends were with him while he was ill, he felt bored and lonely. So one day he had an idea. He decided to invite all the animals of China to visit him. Now China is an enormous country with the tallest mountains, the longest rivers and the thickest jungles, and many, many animals live there.

月 4 日

As China is so vast, the Buddha sent three apsaras to carry his message to the animals. Apsaras are flying women with magical powers, and they reached China flying down through the clouds from their home in the heavens in no time at all. The first apsara went to a farm in the very middle of China where Rat, Cat, Dog, Pig, Rooster and Water Buffalo lived.

Rat was a clever creature who liked to be sure of getting her dinner. She lived in the rafters of the farmhouse. Whenever sacks of rice were brought in from the paddy fields she would scamper down the wooden beams to eat any grains of rice that were spilled. No one minded her taking the grain. She showed that there was plenty of food in the house and the farmers believed she brought them good luck.

Cat was also fond of living in the house, but this was because he was extremely lazy. He spent his days sleeping in the kitchen next to the warm stove. This annoyed Rat, who scampered around Cat collecting food for them both.

Dog was not allowed indoors. She was a friendly animal who stood at the gate and barked when strangers passed by.

In the yard Pig dozed in the summer sun and dreamed about her supper. Would there be leftover rice noodles or perhaps some spicy beancurd?

Rooster, like roosters everywhere, pecked in the dust looking for food, but in the evening he would tell Pig, Rat and Cat exciting stories about his past adventures.

Water Buffalo lived out in the watery paddy fields where the rice was grown. He pulled the plough in the fields and the cart to market, and happily gave children rides on his broad brown back.

The second apsara travelled all the way to the jungle-covered mountains
and fast-flowing rivers in the distant south west of China where Tiger, Hare,

月 8 日

Dragon and Snake made their homes, far away from the farmhouse and rice paddies.

Tiger lived deep inside the jungle, while Hare lived nearby in the grassy valley. Hare took care to stay out of Tiger's way as he was rather timid, and Tiger was quick to lose her temper.

Every night, when Tiger was asleep, Hare would gaze at the watery, white moon, dreaming of what it would be like to live there.

Snake could change her shape and sometimes, when nobody was looking, she would turn into a young girl. When the sun was high in the sky she would lie on the warm rocks near the water, but at night she would sometimes slither into a house, wind herself around the rafters and fall asleep.

Dragon seemed to be a mixture of many different animals. He had the ears of a water buffalo, the horns of a deer and the scales of a fish. His tiger's feet had four long claws like those of the hawk. Dragon lived in a luxurious palace deep down at the bottom of the river. He could fly in the air and when he breathed, droplets of water showered out of his mouth and fell to the earth as rain. He, too, could change his shape, and become as tiny as a silkworm or as huge as a black bear.

The third apsara went to the great, grassy plains far away in Northern China, where Horse and Sheep lived together. Here, a cold wind always

blew down from the North Pole and even though the sun shone every day in summer, it was rarely hot.

Horse had a thick, dappled coat and a long, glossy mane and tail. He was always tossing his head or flicking his tail to show them off. Although short and stocky he could gallop for many, many miles without getting tired, and all he needed to eat at night was the lush, green grass.

Sheep also had a thick, shaggy coat to keep him warm. He did not travel far but loved to gaze at the clouds scudding across the big sky, the distant snow-clad mountains, and the setting sun.

Monkey lived everywhere. She jumped from tree to tree in the tall, dark jungle and watched Tiger and Hare far below. She scampered into the fields to tease Water Buffalo and disturbed Cat in his cosy farmhouse. Monkey had even been up to the moon and met the queen who lived there – but that is another story.

Cat was settling down on his favourite spot next to the stove when the first apsara arrived with the message from Buddha inviting the animals to his home. 'I'm just going to have a little doze,' Cat told Rat. 'Wake me up when it's time to go.' And with this he curled up into a tight little ball and fell fast asleep.

Water Buffalo, who walked rather slowly and always worried about being late, started off almost at once. One by one, the other animals followed.

First came Tiger, out of the dense, dark jungle. Moon-white Hare waited quietly until Tiger was a long way in front before bounding out of his hole. Dragon was not frightened of anybody. He emerged from deep down in his watery kingdom where he had been planning a violent rainstorm. He pranced along, occasionally flying up into the air and dousing everyone with water.

Snake slid quietly behind Dragon on her smooth, pale belly, unconcerned by the cool drops of water. Horse, who came next, was not at all pleased to get wet. He shook his mane and stamped his hoof, but he was too good-natured to be angry for long. Sheep, who walked beside him, smiled to himself and thought of the fresh, green grass back home.

Monkey was as mischievous as usual. She ran backwards and forwards among the long line of animals, pulling Horse's tail and making silly faces at Hare. Monkey annoyed Hare so much he almost lost his temper.

月20日

Rooster kept stopping to peck at grain so often he almost got left behind. Then Dog would bark at his feet to make him run fast to catch up with the animals in front.

Pig was sorry to be so far away from her delicious leftovers, but as she enjoyed adventures and being with the other animals, she was perfectly happy ambling behind them. But she was not the last in the long line of animals.

月 22 日

The last animal of all was Rat. But where was Cat?

Had Rat forgotten to wake Cat, or had she deliberately let him carry on sleeping? Who can tell? But Cat remained fast asleep by the stove while all the other animals set out on their long journey to see Buddha in bed.

The animals travelled for many days and many nights. Every morning Rooster would wake them up as the sun rose. Every evening they would stop to eat their supper and tell stories. And in the middle of the night, when everyone else was asleep, Hare crept quietly away and gazed for hours at the moon.

One day, Rat ran past all the other ten animals until she came to Water Buffalo. 'I am such a tiny little creature,' she pleaded. 'My legs are so short and I am so tired. May I have a ride on your big, broad back?' Water Buffalo was a friendly animal and immediately agreed. With this, Rat climbed up and sat on his shoulders. All day she stared straight ahead between his horns as he lumbered towards the Buddha's home.

月 2 5 日

Late, late in the afternoon, Rat finally saw Buddha's home in the distance. At once she scampered down Water Buffalo's broad back and ran as fast as she could to be the first to arrive at Buddha's House.

'How glad I am to see you,' Buddha said, as she raced in. Suddenly, as he watched the animals coming towards him, he had a wonderful idea. 'I will name the years after all the animals,' he announced. 'And Rat, because you have arrived first among all the animals,' he continued, 'I am going to name the first year after you. From now on this year shall be called the year of the rat.' Rat was delighted.

A little while afterwards, Water Buffalo came plodding in, annoyed that Rat had raced ahead. 'Welcome,' said Buddha. 'Because you are the second animal to arrive, I shall name the second year after you.' Water Buffalo was

so pleased to have a year named after him that he forgot to be angry at Rat's trick. And so the second year was called the year of the water buffalo.

And then, one by one, as the other animals wearily arrived, each was given the name of a year. The third year was the year of the tiger. Then

came the years of the hare, the dragon, the snake, the horse, the sheep, the monkey, the rooster, the dog and the pig. Twelve years were thus named.

月 3 3 日

But when it got to the thirteenth year Cat was nowhere to be seen. He was still fast asleep in his favourite warm spot by the stove and for this reason there is no year named after the cat. The Chinese say that Cat never forgave Rat for not waking him up, and this is why, ever since that summer's day in China hundreds of years ago, Cat and Rat have been enemies.

THE STORY OF THE
CHINESE ZODIAC

This story about the animal zodiac probably became widespread in China in about 600 AD, after Buddhism had become established. It certainly shows Indian influences, especially in the inclusion of the rat and the monkey – animals which figure in many Indian stories. The story is neither fixed nor elaborate, and I have added several embellishments for this version.

Although animals had been associated with years previously in China, it was only about this time that the correlation became systematic. The twelve animals were combined with the existing Chinese system of five elements – wood, fire, earth, metal and water – to make a cycle of sixty years. Thus, for example, 1984 was the year of the wood rat and the start of the present cycle. 1996 is the year of the fire rat, 2008 the earth rat, 2020 the metal rat and 2032 the water rat. The cycle will end in 2043 with the year of the water pig.

Each animal is associated with certain personality traits. The rat, for example, is said to be clever at making money, and the water buffalo to be dependable. Children are expected to have the traits of the animal of the year they are born. Some years are considered more favourable than others, and there is also a difference depending on whether the child is a boy or girl. It is considered extremely fortunate to give birth to a boy in the year of the dragon as it is believed he will grow up to occupy a very high position, perhaps even become emperor. However, to be born in the horse year is believed in traditional China to be unlucky for girls since they will be independent-minded and find it difficult to get married. As in the western zodiac, some animals are better matched as marriage partners than others and matchmakers used to take account of this.

The traditional Chinese year follows a lunar calendar and so New Year falls in late January or early February. New Year's Day is celebrated with great festivity, and it is common for people to send cards featuring the animal linked to the New Year.

The Animals' Qualities

RAT

1948, 1960, 1972, 1984, 1996

People born in the year of the rat are talented at making money. Although careful with their money, they are not miserly and may be extremely generous to friends. They make their fortunes by working very hard and by steady accumulation, just as the rat scurries around all day accumulating small amounts of food. Their ambition is cloaked by humility and although capable of real anger, they are able to control it. Indeed, rats are not always as quiet or reserved as they first appear.

WATER BUFFALO

1949, 1961, 1973, 1985, 1997

The water buffalo is deliberate and slow-moving and those born in his year exhibit these qualities. They will work hard and prosper by fortitude and perseverance. Their logical minds are evident in the way they carry out their work. Appearing rather quiet, they are in fact very alert and hold strong views. It is not difficult to goad them into rage. They do not always display their feelings, especially to loved ones, but they make very good friends and always keep their promises.

TIGER

1950, 1962, 1974, 1986, 1998

As might be expected, people born in the year of the tiger are strong and brave. They are also restless and prone to stray, especially in marriage, as in traditional China it was believed that the tiger could run a thousand miles and back in one night. They are quick to act but sometimes make hasty decisions, and can be suspicious and bad-tempered. But these are minor faults because, at heart, the tiger person is generous, affectionate and sincere.

HARE

1951, 1963, 1975, 1987, 1999

In traditional Chinese belief the hare is associated with the moon and people born in this year display several qualities indicative of this. Although rather timid at times, they are ambitious and financially astute. They also possess an unusual appreciation of beauty: they dress well, have excellent manners and their graciousness makes them many friends with whom they like to gossip, although they never deliberately say anything to hurt others. They always think before they act but are sometimes over-cautious. The hare person can occasionally feel melancholy, but rarely gets angry.

DRAGON

1952, 1964, 1976, 1988, 2000

The dragon is the symbol of imperial power in China and is therefore renowned for strength, virtue and magnanimity. People born in this year are energetic and brave, and are expected to accomplish much in their lives, often devoting their energies to worthy causes but also likely to become wealthy. They can be excitable and talkative, but are never malicious. Despite their fierce appearance, they are sensitive and tender-hearted. They are also excellent at inspiring confidence in others.

SNAKE

1953, 1965, 1977, 1989, 2001

The snake is the most profound thinker of all the animals and people born in the year of the snake will therefore be wise. They are often beautiful and will always look elegant although they may also be rather vain about their appearance, They enjoy the finer aspects of life: books, music, the arts and good food. Seemingly serene, they are intense people who rely on their own opinions in their determination to succeed. Their compassionate nature leads them at times to be over-solicitous.

HORSE

1954, 1966, 1978, 1990, 2002

The horse is considered a handsome animal. People born in this year are attractive to others and like to dress up in fine, colourful clothes. They enjoy large social gatherings and their easy nature makes them popular. Their intelligence, strength, alertness and independence stand them in good stead and they are often multi-talented. Their quick emotions sometimes make them impatient and quick-tempered. However even though they can be unpredictable, they are always fun to have around.

SHEEP

1955, 1967, 1979, 1991, 2003

Those born in the year of the sheep may not be ambitious, but may have many talents, especially in the arts. The most tender-hearted, kind and generous of the animals they are loved by everyone, although some people may take advantage of them. They readily forgive the faults of others, and are always self-effacing about their own considerable accomplishments. These often manifest themselves in creative work in which the innate good taste of sheep people enables them to become very successful.

MONKEY

1956, 1968, 1980, 1992, 2004

The skill and adaptability of the monkey mean that people born in this year excel at all they choose to do, although they can be arrogant. They are inventive, have excellent memories and enjoy solving puzzles which they do with considerable ease, but they sometimes show a lack of constancy. Because of a strong belief in themselves and their sense of superiority, they are not always good at making friends, although they are very talkative and always valued by others.

ROOSTER

1957, 1969, 1981, 1993, 2005

Those born in the year of the rooster are never shy and often display real bravery. They are industrious but since they have a tendency to take on more than they can cope with they may become frustrated and disappointed. They are not good at taking advice themselves, yet they can be overly critical of others. Nevertheless, they enjoy telling amusing stories so that people find them interesting and fun to be with.

DOG

1958, 1970, 1982, 1994, 2006

The loyalty and affection of dogs makes those born in this year very popular people, although they shy away from large gatherings. They are trustworthy and make loyal friends, although they do not hold back from criticising others. They have a passion for fair play. They will act upon their beliefs with a zeal and a determination which can border on stubbornness, but they always remain calm even under stress.

PIG

1959, 1971, 1983, 1995, 2007

The pig is considered to be very brave but rather head-strong. Thus, people born in this year sometimes act without thinking; this gets them into situations which they later regret. It is very difficult to deflect them at the time as they are very opinionated and do not often care to seek advice. They may lose their temper, but as they hate quarrels they are quick to reconcile disputes. They never bear grudges and their friends are friends for life.

ILLUSTRATOR'S NOTE

As a child growing up in Africa, turning over a stone to discover what lay beneath was always an exciting activity for me. I still enjoy turning over stones, and illustrating *The Legend of the Chinese Zodiac* was no exception.

In researching the images for this book, I was inspired by the grace of the apsaras in the ancient frescoes of the caves of Dunhuang, on the Silk Road, and by the quiet, mystical qualities of Chinese silk paintings. I expected Chinese woodcuts to be hard-edged and static. However, I was surprised to find that they were characterised by energetic, often flowing, lines. The oldest woodcut found to date, 'The Diamond Sutra', is a fine example of this. Even when I found no obvious movement in a print, I discovered subtle expressions that suggested a wave of communication between the subjects. I also found that artists knew how to use strong outlines while capturing a sense of movement. These are the qualities that I have set out to capture in my watercolour illustrations.

The colours I have chosen are arguably over-intense, particularly as it is claimed that many Chinese painters were against the use of significant amounts of colour. However, I have only adopted the range found in examples of Chinese painting and porcelain I have seen. I am sure that in many instances original colours have faded, just as they have faded on old European paintings and tapestries.

The illustrations in *The Legend of the Chinese Zodiac* are certainly not an attempt to imitate Chinese art. However, while working on this book it has been a pleasure to watch the influence of the Chinese tradition seep through into my work. This cross-fertilisation has been an exciting and enriching process for me.

Philippa-Alys Browne
Harare, Zimbabwe, 1997

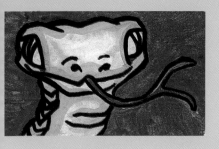   

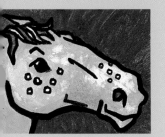

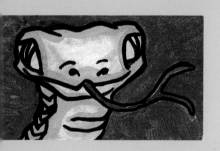  

SUSAN WHITFIELD is a historian of China who has lived and worked there and visits regularly. She has written and edited many books and articles on China and works for the British Library on ancient Chinese manuscripts. She was born in the year of the rat but owns a cat, and they get on extremely well.

PHILIPPA-ALYS BROWNE has created four books on animals: *African Animals ABC* (Barefoot Books, 1995), praised by the *Times Educational Supplement* for its 'Stunning watercolour illustrations, weaving richly-coloured tribal patterns into the animal shape'; *A Gaggle of Geese* (Barefoot Books, 1995); *Kangaroos Have Joeys* (Barefoot Books, 1996), about which *Nursery World* said 'The visual impact of this book will make adults and infants alike sit up and take notice'; and *Elephants and Emus* (Barefoot Books, 1997), commended by *Montessori Education* for its 'Vivid imagery, appealing rhyme and rhythm and ready humour. The illustrations grab the attention of even the most wayward child'.
Philippa-Alys's work has been widely exhibited and her books have been translated into several languages. She divides her time between the UK and Zimbabwe.

BAREFOOT BOOKS publishes high-quality picture books for children of all ages and specialises in material from different cultures. For a copy of our current catalogue, please contact our London office — tel: 0171 704 6492; fax: 0171 359 5798; e-mail: sales@barefoot-books.com; website: www.barefoot-books.com